# the Fratellis
## Costello Music

# HENRIETTA

## Written by The Fratellis

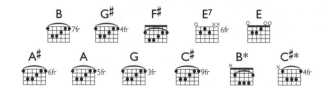

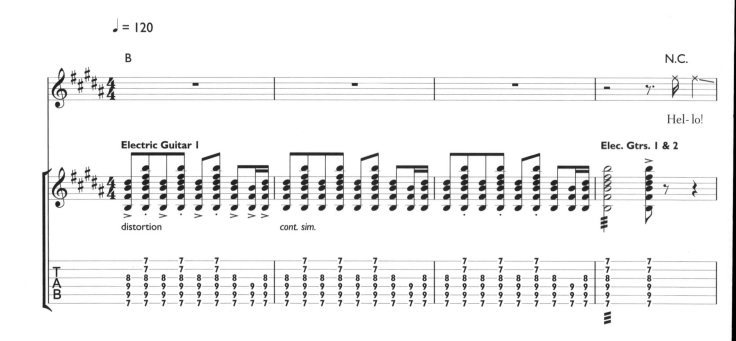

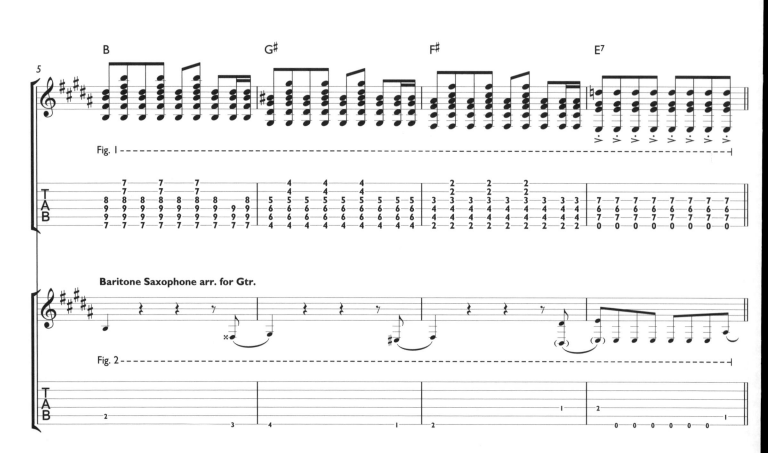

8

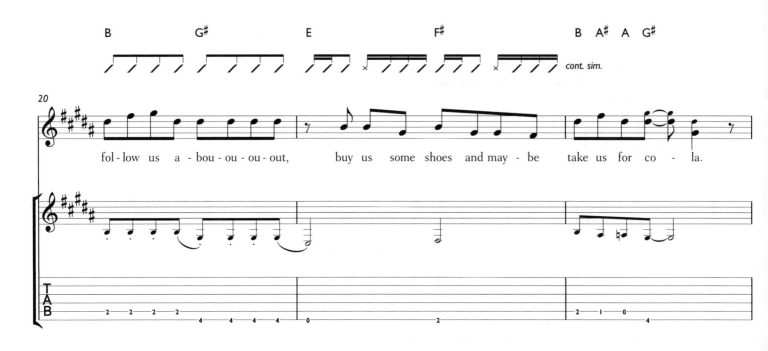

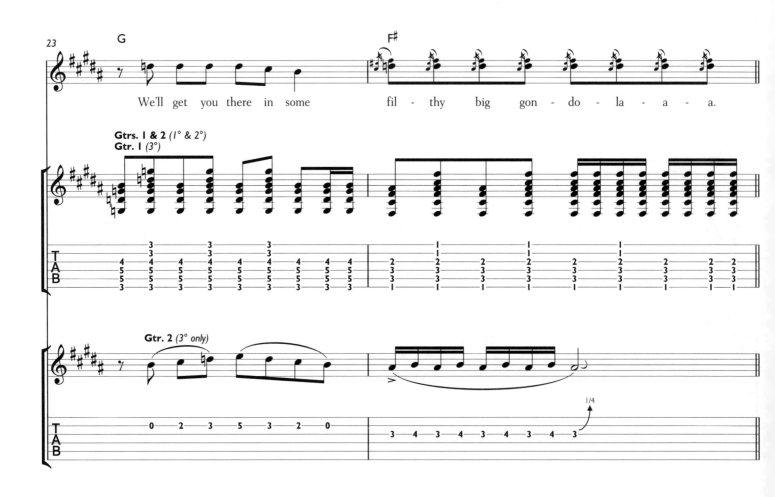

10

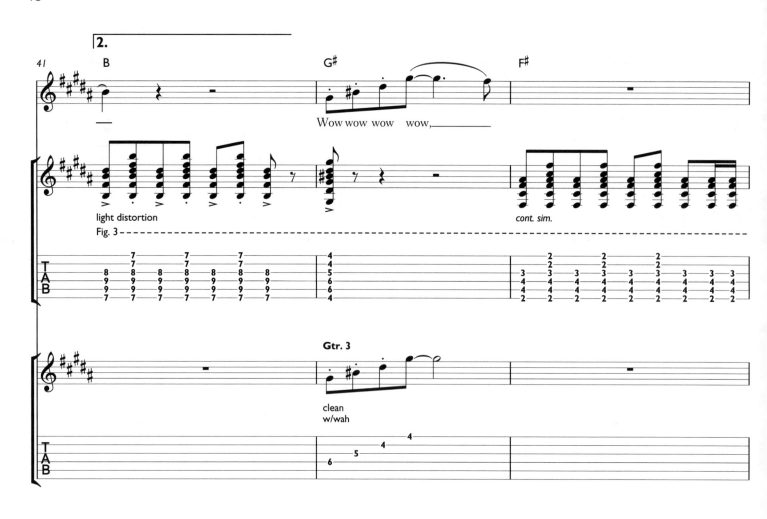

**Coda**

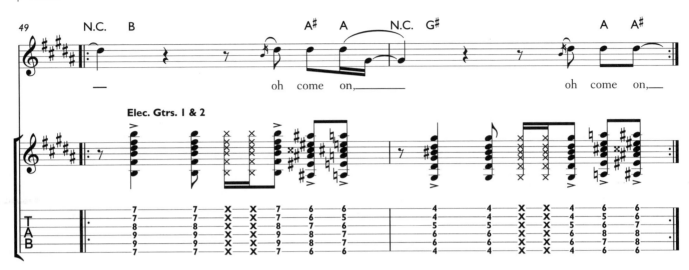

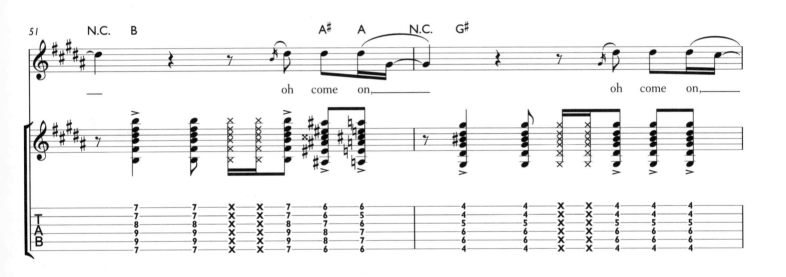

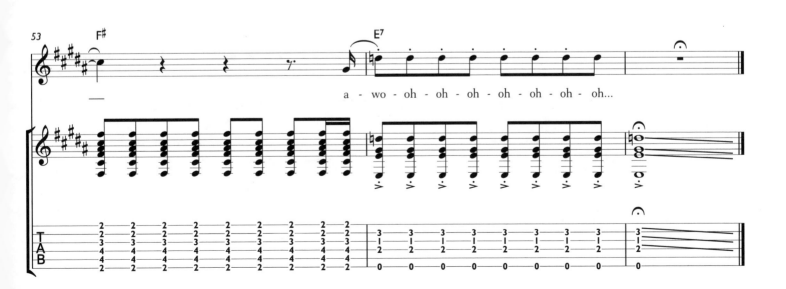

# FLATHEAD

Written by The Fratellis

14

electric w/ slight crunch

(sing 2° only)

And she said the

(Ah, _____ ah.) _____

boy's not right in the head, so you stood and said: "Oh my God!" Till she said...

clean

(sing 3° & 4 ° only)

(Ba-ra ra oh_____ ba-ra oh...) Repeat x4

(Ba-ra bap ba-ra ra, ra, ra, ba-ra bap ba-ra ra, ra, ra, ba-ra bap ba-ra ra, ra, ra, ba-ra bap-ba-ra ra, ra, ra...

Repeat x4

*Elec. Gtrs. 1 & 2 play Figs. 4 & 3*

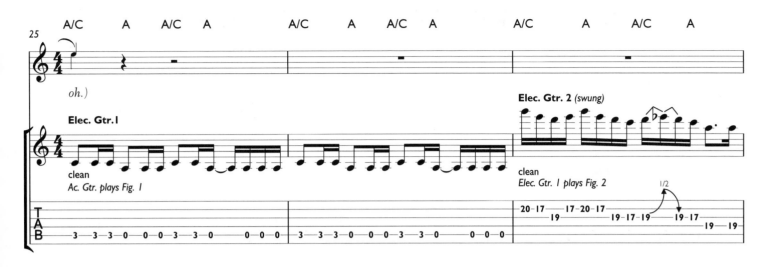

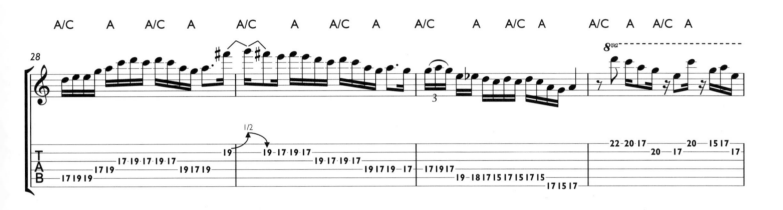

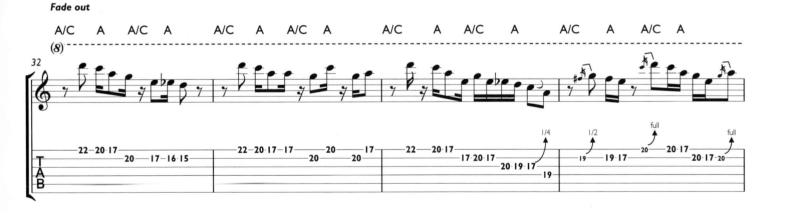

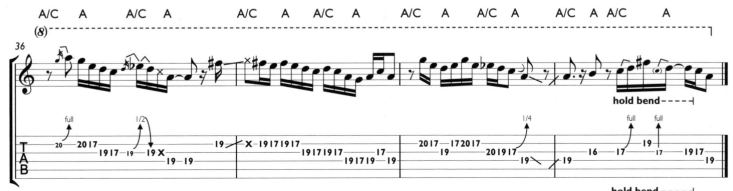

# CUNTRY BOYS & CITY GIRLS

## Written by The Fratellis

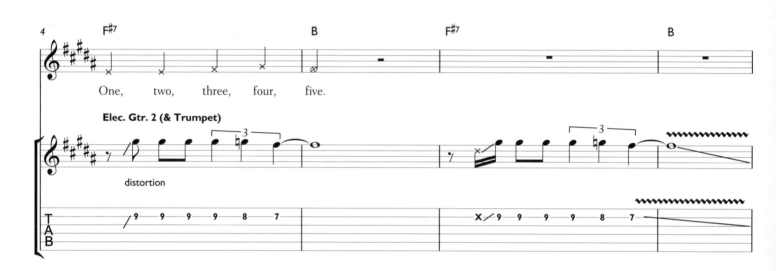

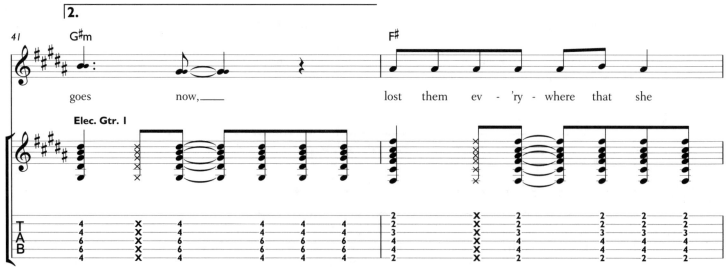

# WHISTLE FOR THE CHOIR

Written by The Fratellis

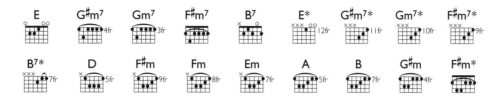

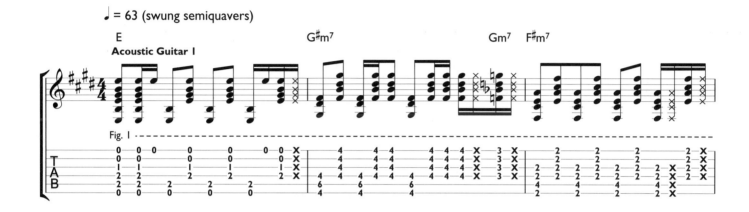

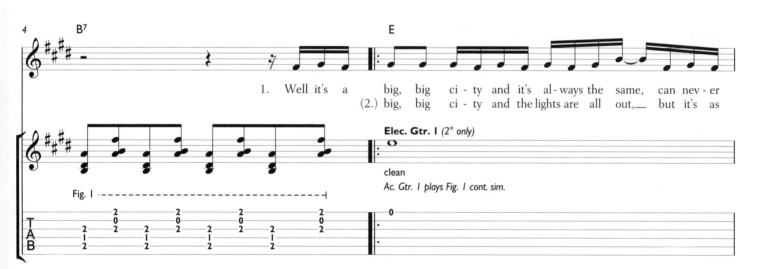

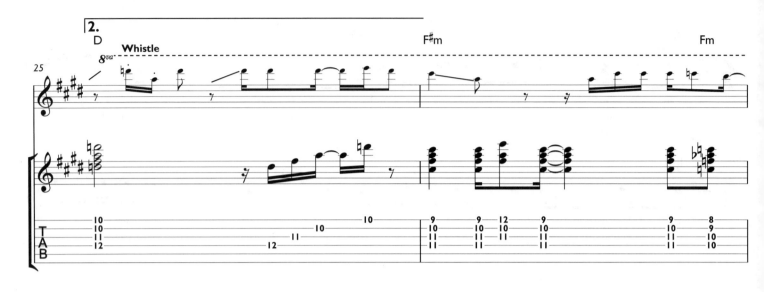

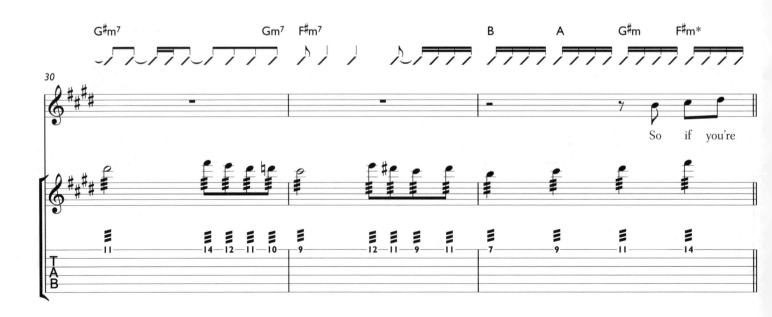

# CHELSEA DAGGER

## Written by The Fratellis

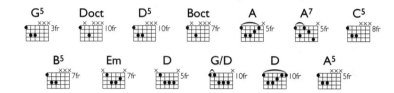

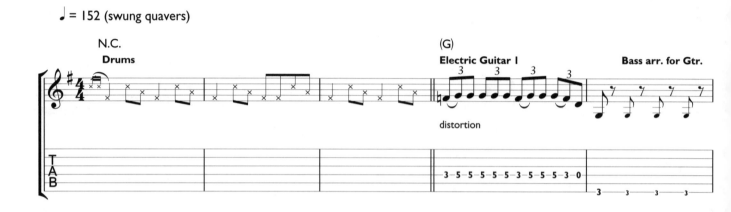

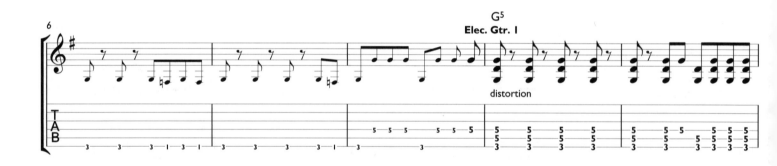

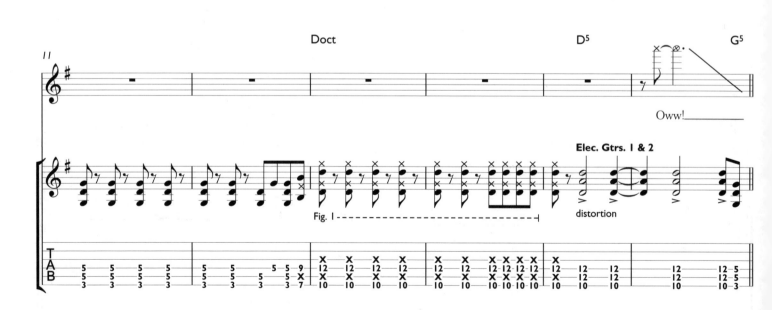

29

# FOR THE GIRL

Written by The Fratellis

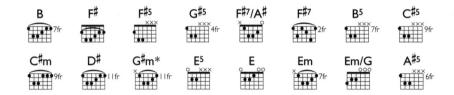

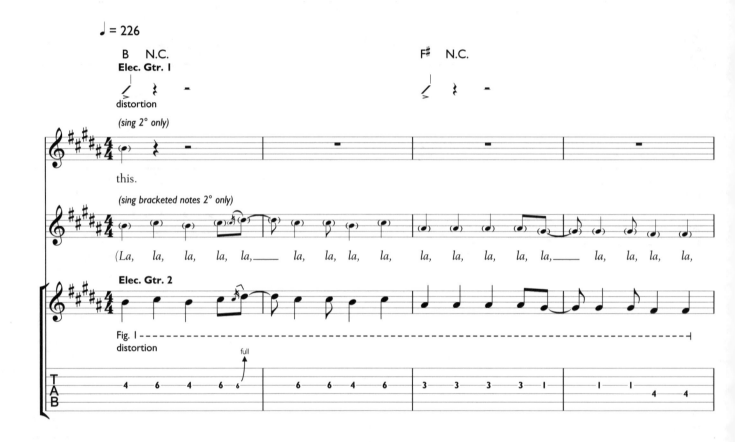

young love plea - ses you ea - sy, makes you sick in a bad way. And
She said take me to Lon - don, tell me some - thing I don't know.

all the while the girl sang, la la la la, she sang,

kick - in's for my sweet - heart, bruis - es that I

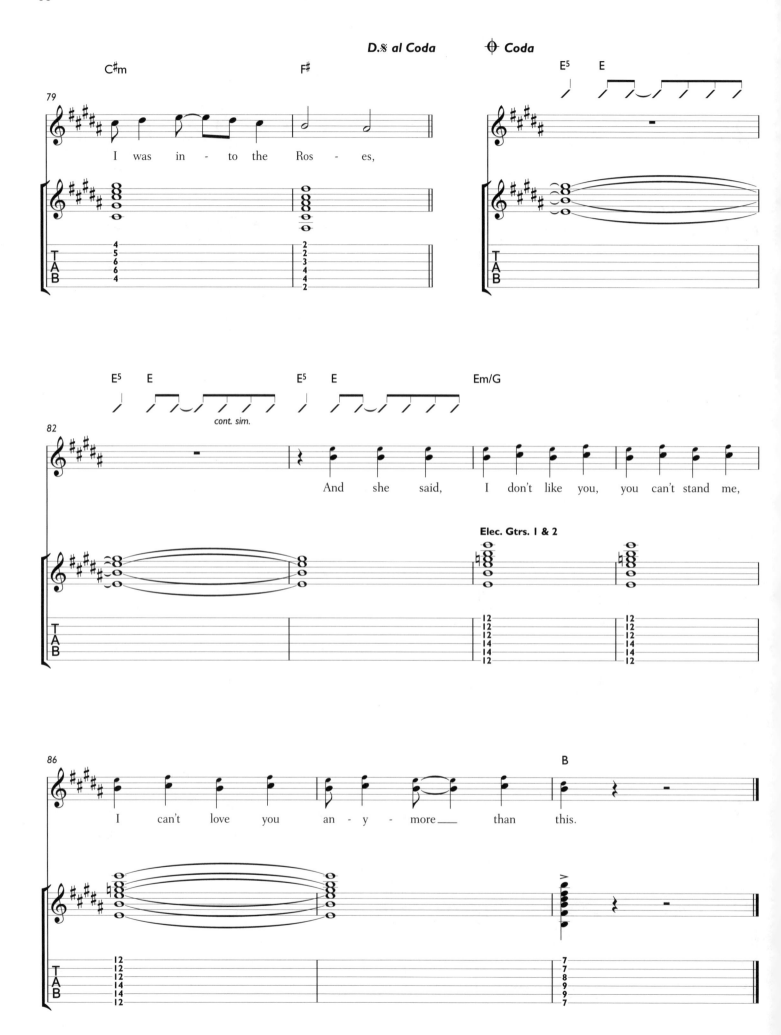

# DOGINABAG

Written by The Fratellis

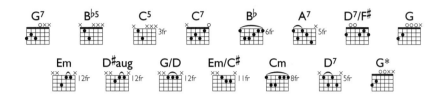

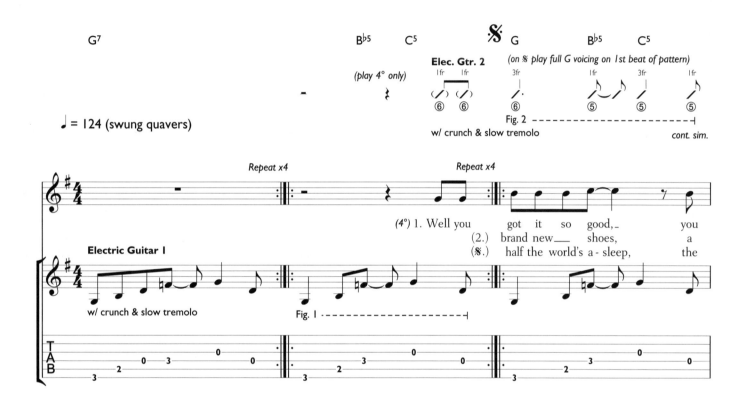

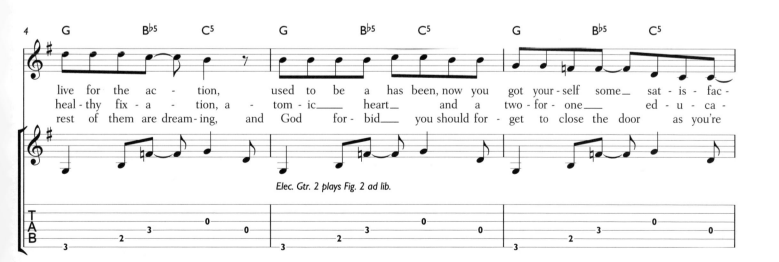

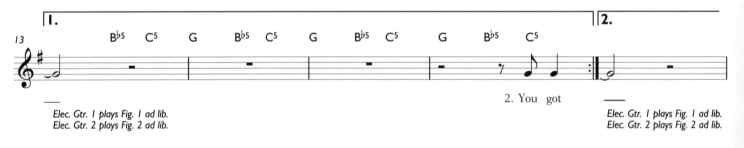

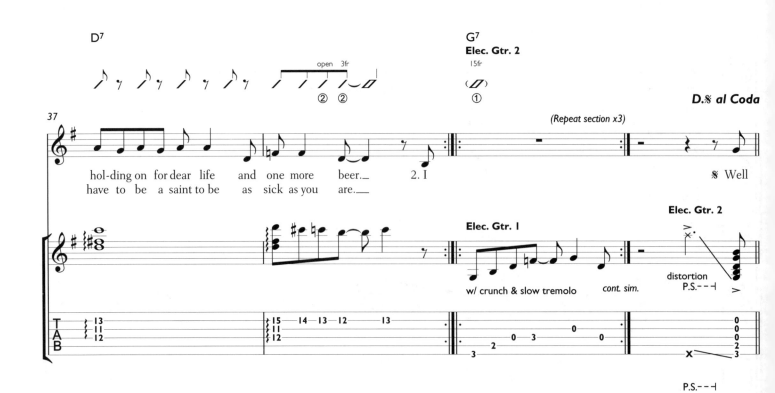

With your dog in a bag— sleep-ing next to your rid - i - cu-lous mind,—

with your dog in a bag— sleep-ing next to your rid - i - cu - lous mind.

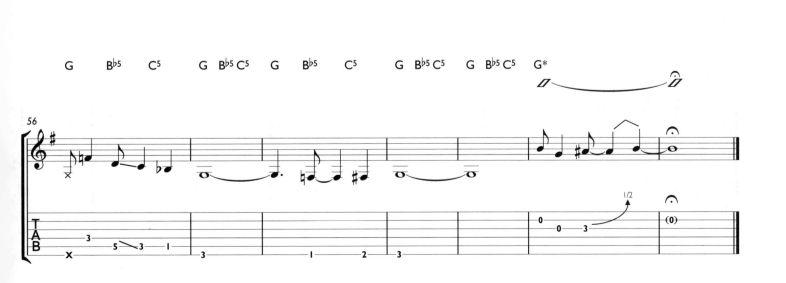

# CREEPIN UP THE BACKSTAIRS

Written by The Fratellis

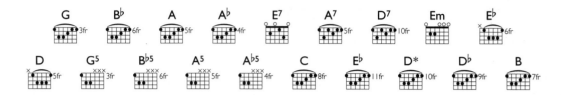

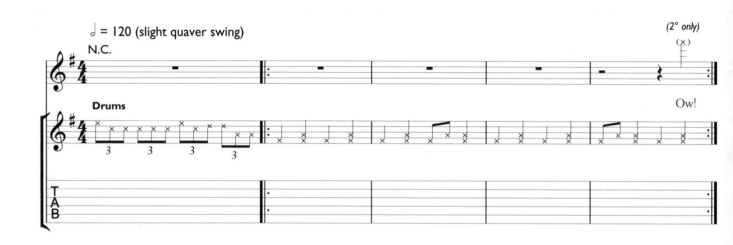

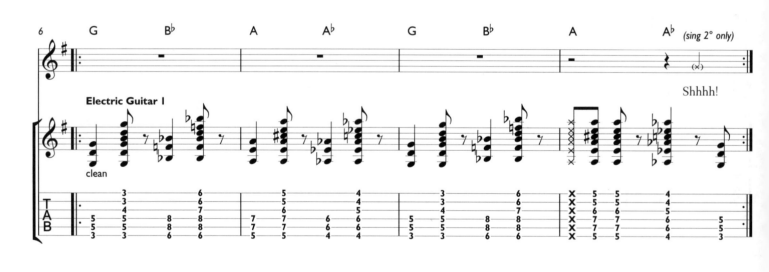

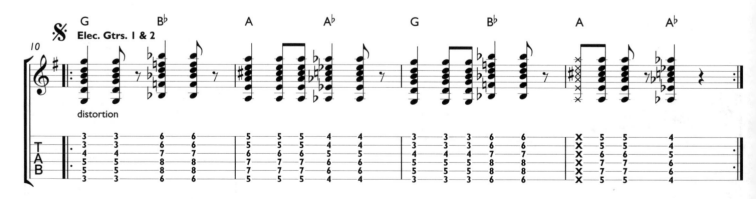

44

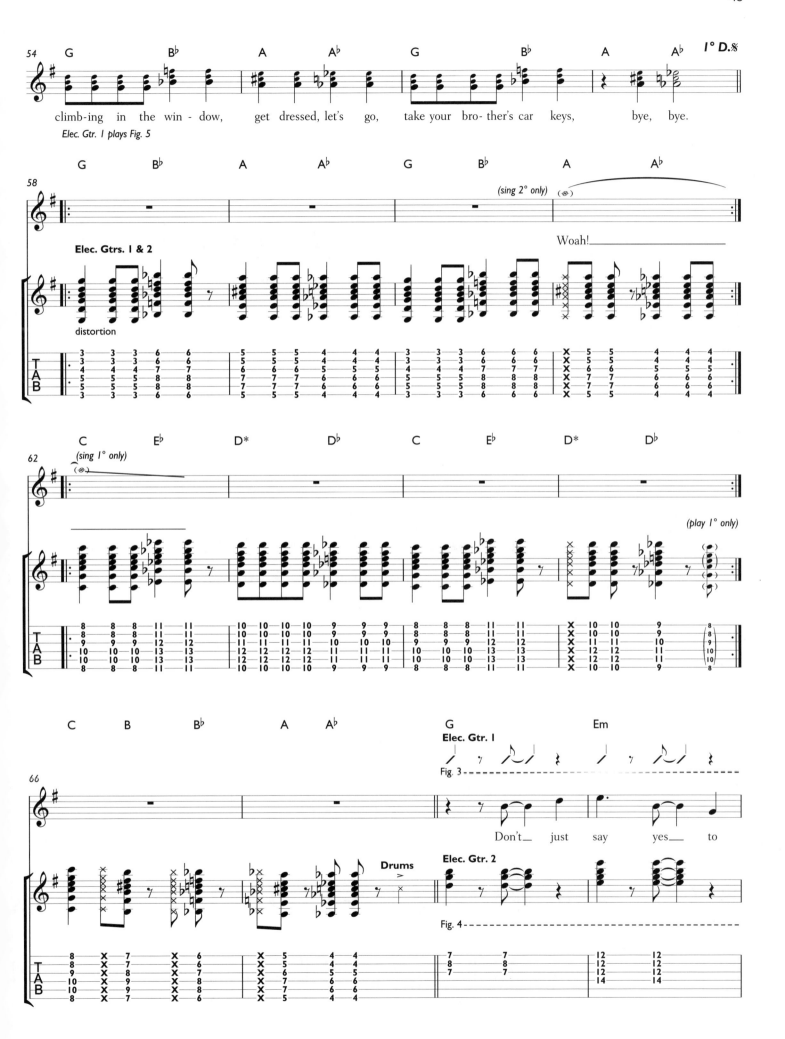

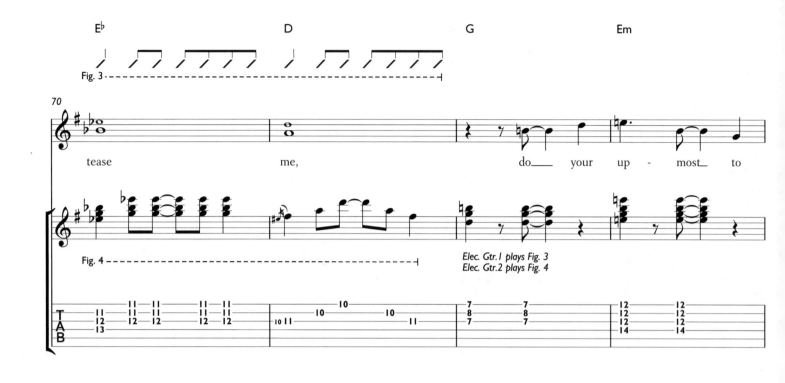

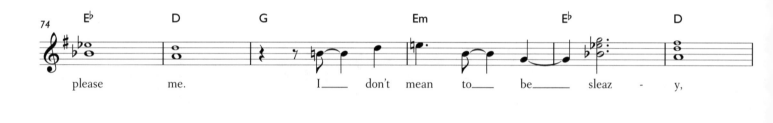

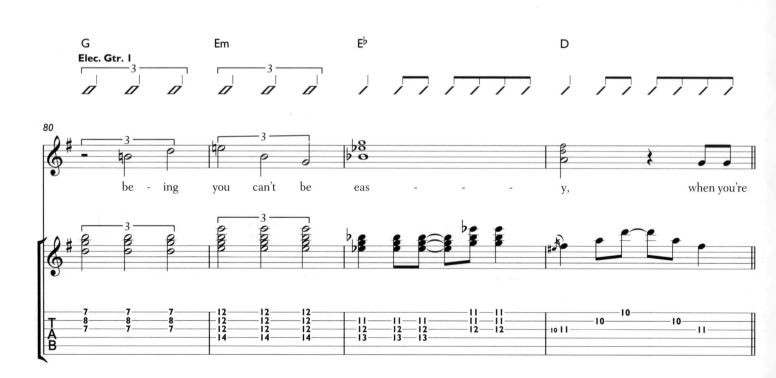

# VINCE THE LOVEABLE STONER

Written by The Fratellis

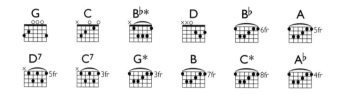

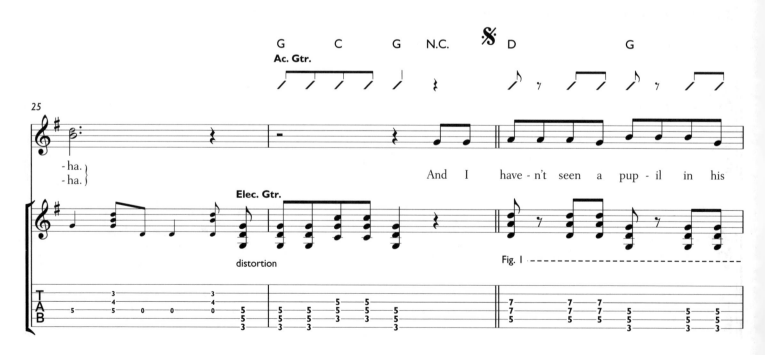

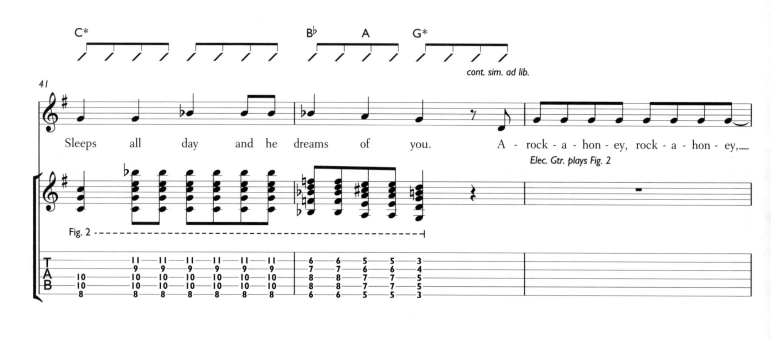

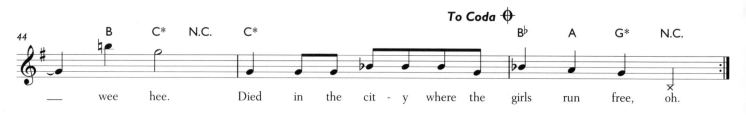

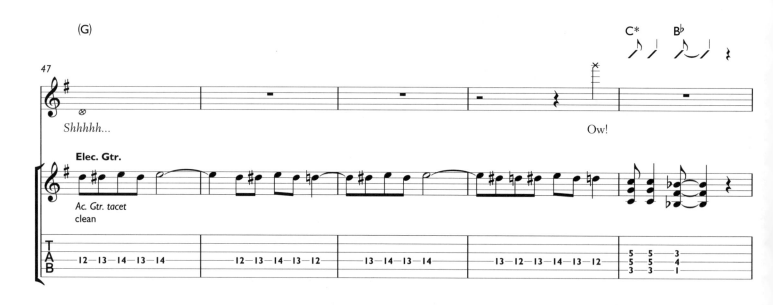

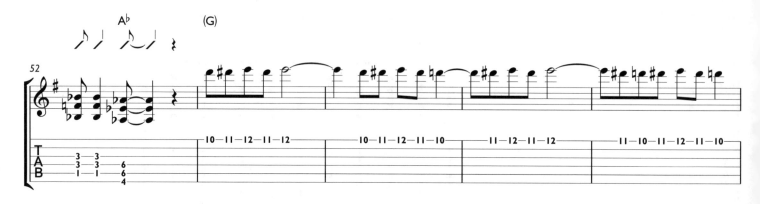

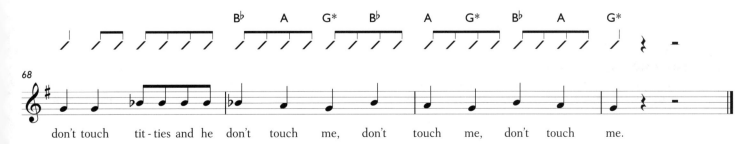

# EVERYBODY KNOWS
# YOU CRIED LAST NIGHT

Written by The Fratellis

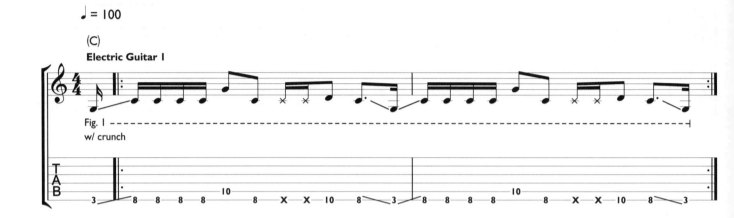

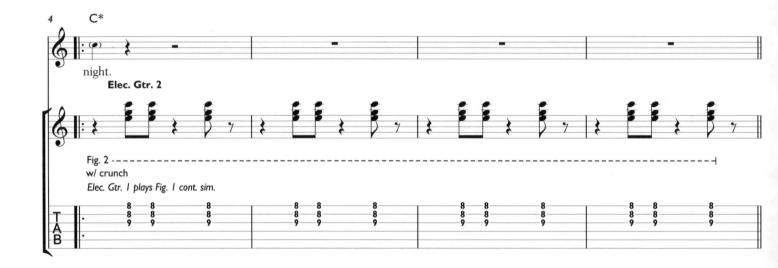

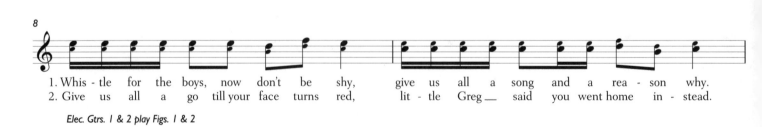

1. Whis-tle for the boys, now don't be shy, give us all a song and a rea-son why.
2. Give us all a go till your face turns red, lit-tle Greg___ said you went home in-stead.

*Elec. Gtrs. 1 & 2 play Figs. 1 & 2*

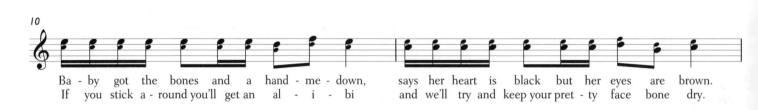

Ba - by got the bones and a hand - me - down, says her heart is black but her eyes are brown.
If you stick a - round you'll get an al - i - bi and we'll try and keep your pret - ty face bone dry.

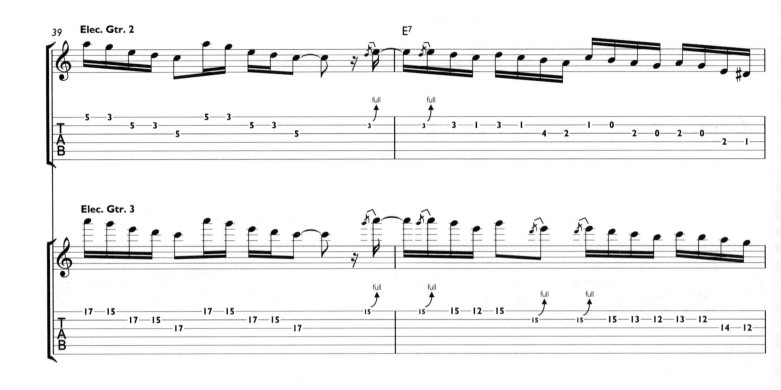

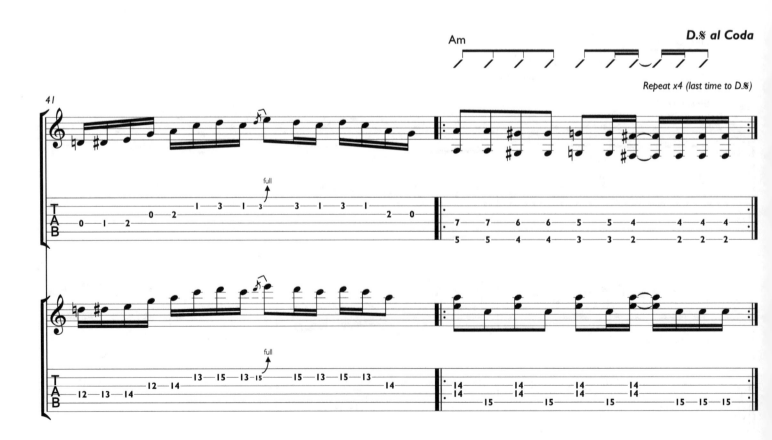

⊕ **Coda**

night.                                                        Ev - 'ry - bod - y    knows__  you  cried__  last

*Repeat x4*                                          *Repeat x3*

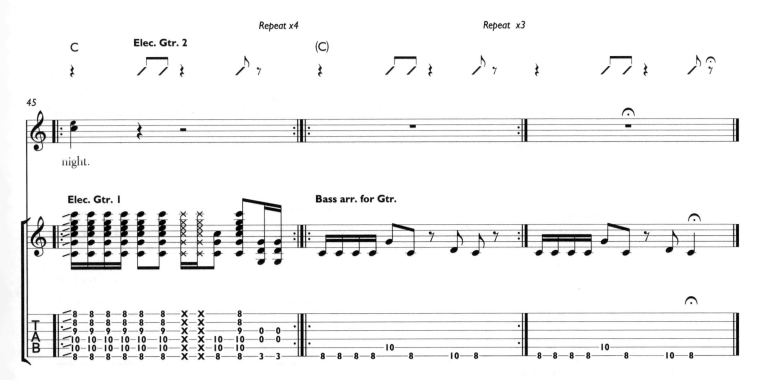

night.

# BABY FRATELLI

### Written by The Fratellis

# GOT MA NUTS FROM A HIPPY

Written by The Fratellis

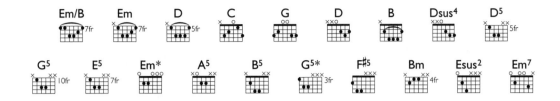

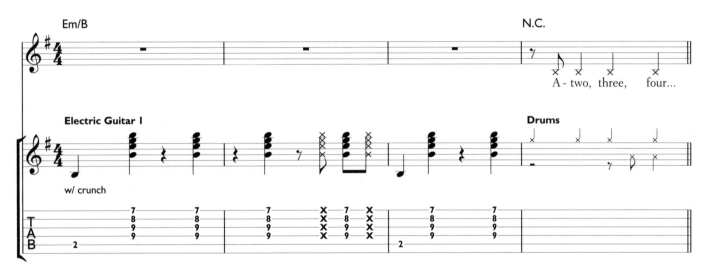

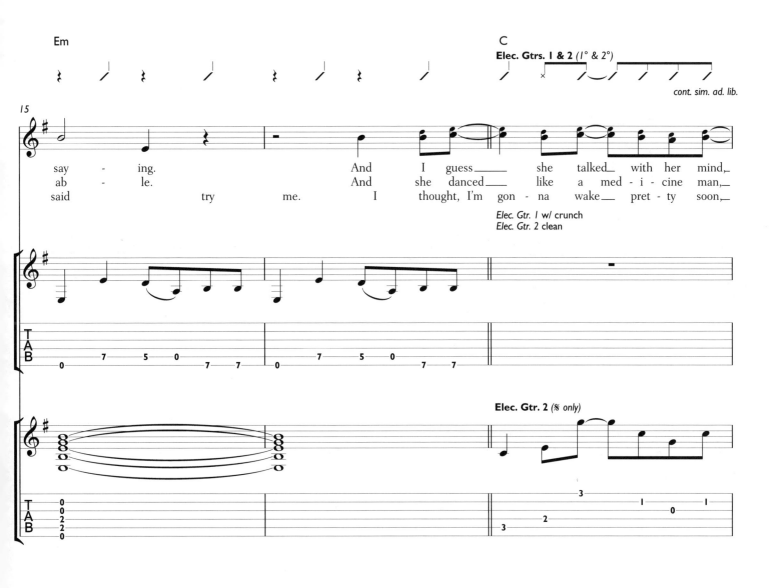

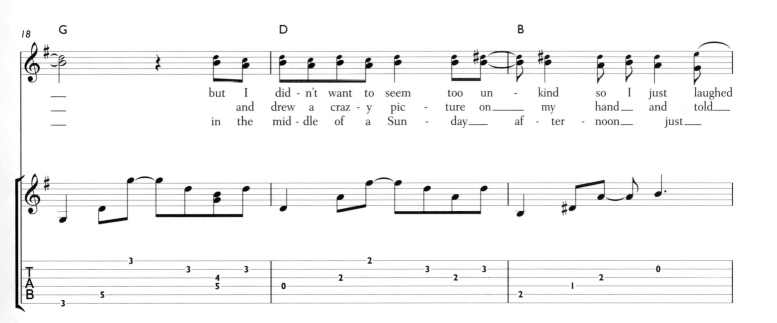

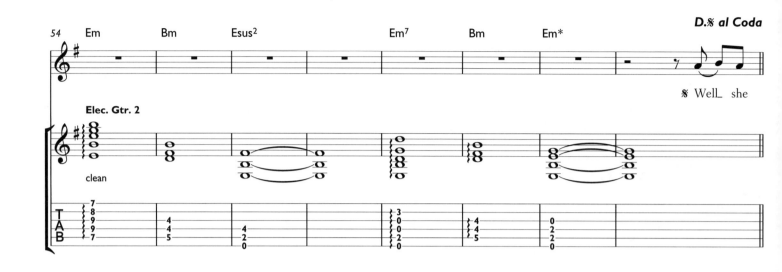

*D.%̸ al Coda*

54 Em    Bm    Esus² · · · · · · · Em⁷    Bm    Em*

% Well she

⊕ *Coda*

62 D

when she made me a real

66 Em

N.C.    D⁵

Elec. Gtr. 1
Elec. Gtr. 2    all Gtrs. w/ dist
D

man.

She made me

# OLE BLACK 'N' BLUE EYES

Written by The Fratellis

# Notation and Tablature explained

## Understanding chord boxes

Chord boxes show the neck of your guitar as if viewed head on—the vertical lines represent the strings (low E to high E, from left to right), and the horizontal lines represent the frets.

An **X** above a string means 'don't play this string'.
An **O** above a string means 'play this open string'.
The black dots show you where to put your fingers.

A curved line joining two dots on the fretboard represents a 'barre'. This means that you flatten one of your fingers (usually the first) so that you hold down all the strings between the two dots at the fret marked.

A fret marking at the side of the chord box shows you where chords that are played higher up the neck are located.

## Tuning your guitar

The best way to tune your guitar is to use an electronic tuner. Alternatively, you can use relative tuning; this will ensure that your guitar is in tune with itself, but won't guarantee that you will be in tune with the original track (or any other musicians).

## How to use relative tuning

Fret the low E string at the 5th fret and pluck; compare this with the sound of the open A string. The two notes should be in tune. If not, adjust the tuning of the A string until the two notes match.

Repeat this process for the other strings according to this diagram:

Note that the B string should match the note at the 4th fret of the G string, whereas all the other strings match the note at the 5th fret of the string below.

As a final check, ensure that the bottom E string and top E string are in tune with each other.

## Detuning and Capo use

If the song uses an unconventional tuning, it will say so clearly at the top of the music, e.g. '6 = D' (tune string 6 to D) or 'detune guitar down by a semitone'. If a capo is used, it will tell you the fret number to which it must be attached. The standard notation will always be in the key at which the song sounds, but the guitar tab will take tuning changes into account. Just detune/add the capo and follow the fret numbers. The chord symbols will show the sounding chord above and the chord you actually play below in brackets.

## Use of figures

In order to make the layout of scores clearer, figures that occur several times in a song will be numbered, e.g. 'Fig. 1', 'Fig. 2', etc. A dotted line underneath shows the extent of the 'figure'. When a phrase is to be played, it will be marked clearly in the score, along with the instrument that should play it.

## Reading Guitar Tab

Guitar tablature illustrates the six strings of the guitar graphically, showing you where you put your fingers for each note or chord. It is always shown with a stave in standard musical notation above it. The guitar tablature stave has six lines, each of them representing a different string. The top line is the high E string, the second line being the B string, and so on. Instead of using note heads, guitar tab uses numbers which show the fret number to be stopped by the left hand. The rhythm is indicated underneath the tab stave. Ex. 1 (below) shows four examples of single notes.

Ex. 2 shows four different chords. The 3rd one (Asus4) should be played as a barre chord at the 5th fret. The 4th chord (C9) is a half, or jazz chord shape. You have to mute the string marked with an 'x' (the A string in this case) with a finger of your fretting hand in order to obtain the correct voicing.

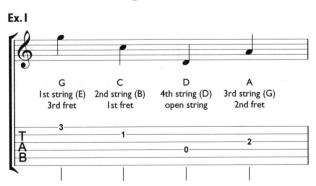

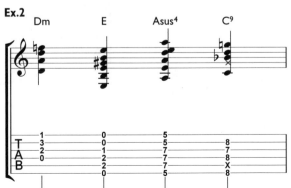

# Notation of other guitar techniques

## Picking hand techniques:

### 1. Down and up strokes
These symbols show that the first and third notes are to be played with a down stroke of the pick and the others up strokes.

### 2. Palm mute
Mute the notes with the palm of the picking hand by lightly touching the strings near the bridge.

### 3. Pick rake
Drag the pick across the indicated strings with a single sweep. The extra pressure will often mute the notes slightly and accentuate the final note.

### 4. Arpeggiated chords
Strum across the indicated strings in the direction of the arrow head of the wavy line.

### 5. Tremolo picking
Shown by the slashes on the stem of the note. Very fast alternate picking. Rapidly and continuously move the pick up and down on each note.

### 6. Pick scrape
Drag the edge of the pick up or down the lower strings to create a scraping sound.

### 7. Right hand tapping
'Tap' onto the note indicated by a '+' with a finger of the picking hand. It is nearly always followed by a pull-off to sound the note fretted below.

### 8. Tap slide
As with tapping, but the tapped note is slid randomly up the fretboard, then pulled off to the following note.

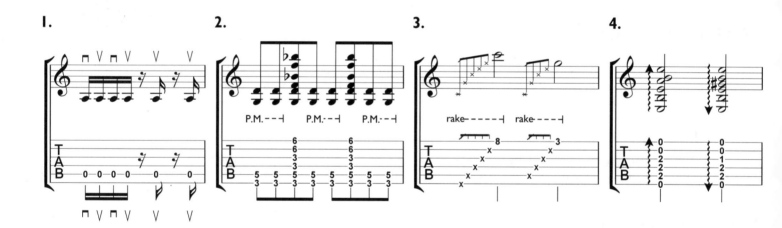

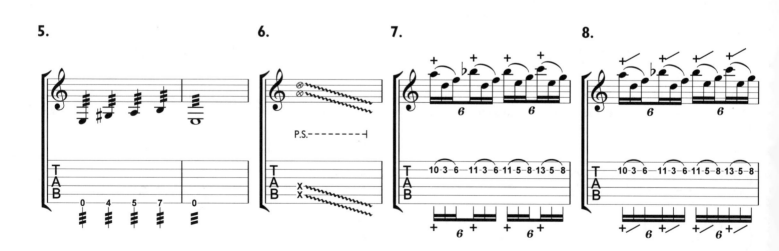